Work This One Out

John, Jack, Joan and Jane are Art Critic, Architect, Acrobat and Aviator, but not necessarily respectively.

The aviator, who is happily married, earns more than his sister, the art critic.

Joan has never heard of "perspective."

John is a misogynist.

Who is the architect?

Many people faced with such a problem have an irresistible impulse to sit down with paper and pencil and discover who the architect was. It is for these enthusiasts that this book has been compiled. If you want to check your result, see Answer #34.

Work This One Out

BY L. H. LONGLEY-COOK

A Crest Reprint

FAWCETT PUBLICATIONS, INC., GREENWICH, CONN.
MEMBER OF AMERICAN BOOK PUBLISHERS COUNCIL, INC.

A Crest Book published by arrangement with
Ernest Benn Ltd., London

First Crest printing, November 1962

Crest Books are published by Fawcett World Library,
67 West 44th Street, New York 36, New York.
Printed in the United States of America.

INTRODUCTION

MATHEMATICAL puzzles are almost as old as mathematics itself. Inevitably, some of the puzzles here presented are old, but the author believes that they have a charm which justifies repetition. Some of the puzzles are old ones in new guises, but most of the puzzles are new.

The author has allowed his friend "Old Prime" to introduce a few of the puzzles with some general comments. "Old Prime" is the actuary of the Colossal Insurance Company. Whether he got his nickname from P' (pronounced P prime), the usual symbol for a life insurance premium, or from his interest in the mathematical puzzles concerning prime numbers, is not known. If, occasionally, "Old Prime" allows his comments to wander somewhat from the problem under discussion, the reader's indulgence is asked as this is typical of "Old Prime."

No attempt has been made to group the puzzles by type since part of the pleasure of mathematical puzzles lies in variety; however, the author has tried to arrange them approximately according to increasing difficulty. The first section is labeled "Quickies," some short problems which are tests of speedy thinking rather than mathematical ability. The later sections are labeled "Easy," "Not So Easy" and "Difficult Puzzles." The "Difficult Puzzles" are difficult in the sense that the reader may take some time to solve them; but the solution of none of the puzzles requires a knowledge of trigonometry, calculus or any other branch of advanced mathematics.   L.H.L-C.

CONTENTS

QUICKIES

1
But Me No Butts

A TRAMP rolls cigarettes from the butts he picks up on the street. He finds that four butts make one new cigarette. How many cigarettes can he smoke from a haul of sixteen butts?

2
Sunday Service

I ALWAYS sit in the same pew at church; the third from the front and the seventh from the back, on the right hand side. Each pew seats 5 persons on each side of the center aisle. What is the total capacity of the church?

3
Fence Me In

I PLAN to fence my frontage on to the main road, which is 100 feet long. Fencing costs $5.00 per 10 feet and posts, which are to be 10 feet apart, cost $5.00 each. What will be the total cost of the fence?

4
Milliner's Problem

A LADY bought a hat with a floral decoration for $10.00. If the hat cost $9.00 more than the decoration, how much did the decoration cost?

5
The Light That Failed

THE LIGHT had failed in our bedroom and my wife asked me to bring her down a pair of stockings. I knew she had 12 identical pairs of light stockings and 12 identical pairs of dark stockings. What was the smallest number of stockings I must collect in order to make sure I brought down a matching pair?

6
Watered Milk

PITCHER A contains a gallon of water, and pitcher B contains a gallon of milk. A cup of water is removed from pitcher A and added to pitcher B, which is then well stirred. A cup of the mixture in pitcher B is now added to pitcher A. Is there more or less milk in pitcher A than water in pitcher B?

7

Cafe au lait

WITH two identical cups of hot coffee, which will cool to drinking temperature first: the one to which cream is added immediately or the one to which the same quantity of cream is added later?

8

As the Cog Moves

TWO EQUAL cog wheels are placed flat on the table with their teeth intermeshed. One is held firm, and the other is moved so that it makes one complete circle of the fixed cog. The teeth of the two cogs are intermeshed throughout. How many times does the moving cog rotate on its own axis during this maneuver?

9

The Rains Came

IN A CERTAIN tropical town ten and a half inches of rain fell in a week and a half. What was the average daily rainfall over the period?

10
High Tide

A LADDER with rungs a foot apart is hanging over the side of a moored boat. At high tide the third rung is just below the water level. If the tide falls one foot, how many rungs are clear of the water?

11
The Christmas Gifts

TWO MOTHERS, Jane and Joan, were buying Christmas-stocking gifts. Each had bought 20 separate gifts for a total of $11.00. Jane bought 5 more gifts for $1.50 and Joan bought one more for 10¢. Which mother has paid the higher average price for her gifts?

12
High Noon

IF IT takes a clock 15 seconds to strike 6 o'clock, how long does it take to strike 12 o'clock?

13
Scaled to Weigh

A PAIR of scales is being used to weigh any number of integral pounds from 1 to 40. What is the minimum number of weights required (1) if weights can be placed only in one pan and (2) if weights can be placed in either pan?

14
Snail's Pace

A SNAIL climbing out of a well advances three feet each day but slips back two feet each night. How many days does it take the snail to climb out if it starts 30 feet below the top of the well?

15
On the Shelf

A BOOKWORM starts at the first page of the first volume of a three-volume work, standing in the usual manner on a bookshelf, and burrows by the shortest route to the last page of the third volume. If the pages of each volume are one inch thick and each cover 1/8 of an inch thick, how far does the bookworm travel?

16
Housing Problem

AN ARCHITECT was asked to design a square house with the window in each wall having a southern exposure. How did he do this?

17
No Radar Trap

I DRIVE at an average speed of 30 miles per hour to the railroad station each morning and just catch my train. On a particular morning there was a lot of traffic and at the halfway point I found I had averaged only 15 miles per hour. How fast must I drive for the rest of the way to catch my train?

18
Round and Round She Goes

THE OUTER track of a phonograph record is 9 inches in diameter and the unused portion in the center is 3 inches in diameter. If the record has 20 grooves to the inch, how far does the needle travel while the record is playing?

19
All Aboard

A TRAIN leaves Neartown for Fartown each hour on the hour, and an identical arrangement applies for the trains from Fartown to Neartown. All trains travel at the same speed. If I travel from Neartown to Fartown, how many trains do I pass if the journey takes 4½ hours?

20
Pound for Pound

ONE END of a rope is attached to a 150-pound weight, the other end, after passing over a pulley, is held by a sailor, who also weighs 150 pounds. Both are stationary and suspended in mid air. If the sailor starts to climb the rope, does the weight go up or down?

21
Around the World

AN AIRPLANE can fly from London to New York in five hours and, since the difference in time between London and New York is five hours, it is possible to arrive in New York at the time you set out from London. With refueling in the air, you could continue to fly around the world at the same speed and reach London at the time you started, which is obviously impossible. How is this explained?

22
Transmutation

WHICH weighs more, a pound of gold or a pound of lead?

23
Family Names

DR. JAMES BROWN is Dr. Leslie Brown's father. Mrs. James Brown is Dr. Leslie Brown's mother. Dr. Leslie Brown is not Dr. James Brown's son. How is this explained?

24
Rocket to Mars

AS PART of a warning device against approaching rockets, the Martians place two electric cables around the equator of Mars, which may be assumed to be a perfect sphere. The first cable is on the ground and is exactly 13,000 miles long. The second cable is raised above the first by closely placed posts each 3 feet 6 inches high. How long is the second cable?

25
Happy Birthday

JOHN and James are twins. John celebrated his fourth birthday today and James celebrates his first birthday tomorrow. How is this explained?

26
Mopping Up

IF 7 MAIDS with 7 mops sweep 7 tons of sand in 7 months, how long does it take 10 maids with 10 mops to sweep 10 tons of sand?

27
Mary's Little Lambs

MARY had some little lambs and so had her friend, Laura. If Mary gave Laura two lambs, they would each have the same number of lambs. If Laura gave Mary two lambs, Mary would have twice as many as Laura. How many lambs did Mary have?

28
Tracing a Figure

WITHOUT lifting the pencil from the paper, or folding the paper, trace out the following figure, going over every line once and only once.

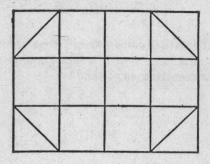

29
My Age

WHEN my son is my age I shall be 5 times his present age and when our combined ages are 50, he will be half my present age. How old am I?

The Little Orchard

OLD PRIME had decided to lay out an orchard in his small garden. He had bought 9 fruit trees and I had expected he would plant four at the corners of a square and the other five at the mid points of the sides and diagonals of the square, thus:

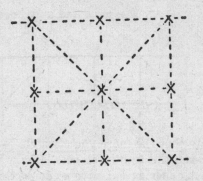

"No," said Old Prime, "in that way there are only 8 lines of three trees. I am sure I can do better than that."

How did he plant them to obtain the maximum number of lines containing 3 trees?

31
Colored Cubes

WITH six different colored paints, we can color each of the six faces of a cube with a different color. The colors can be arranged in various ways to make a number of cubes which are different from each other however we turn them around. How many different colored cubes are possible?

32
The Escalator

"THEY say that the more you struggle in a hangman's noose, the tighter it gets. While I cannot speak from experience, I have no doubt this is so," remarked Old Prime. "I do know that the faster you walk up an escalator, the more steps you have to take. And what is more, this is equally true if you are coming down the escalator. Here is a little problem for you:

"Each step of an escalator is 8 inches above the previous step and the total vertical height of the escalator is 20 feet. The escalator moves up one half step a second. If I step on the lowest step at the moment when it is level with the lower floor and walk up at the rate of one step a second, how many steps do I take to reach the upper floor? (Do not include the steps taken to step on and off the escalator.)"

33
How Old am I?

I AM AS old as John will be when I am twice as old as John was when my age was half the sum of our present ages.

John is as old as I was when John was half the age he will be 10 years hence.

How old am I?

34
Who is the Architect?

JOHN, Jack, Joan and Jane are Art Critic, Architect, Acrobat and Aviator, but not necessarily respectively.

The aviator, who is happily married, earns more than his sister, the art critic.

Joan has never heard of "perspective."

John is a misogynist.

Who is the architect?

35
Chessboard Squares

How MANY squares, of any size, are made by the lines of a standard chessboard?

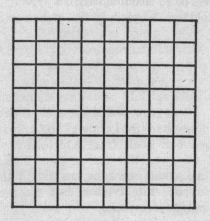

36
A Pile of Paper

I DECIDE to make a pile of paper. The paper I use is one-hundredth (.01) of an inch thick. I first put down a single sheet. Then I double what I have put down, making 2 sheets. A second doubling gives me 4 sheets. A third doubling makes 8 sheets, or eight-hundredths of an inch. If I double the number of sheets thirty times in all, how high is the pile? 10 inches, 100 inches, 1,000 inches, 10,000 inches, 100,000 inches or more?

37
The Three Automobile Numbers

OLD PRIME was more pensive than usual as we walked along the street one day and I asked him what he had on his mind. "I was trying out an idea I received from a British friend. He tells me he obtains a good index of the availability of spending money by noting the number of automobiles with unrepaired body damage which are parked along a certain length of sidewalk. I fear my experiment is not working out well here as I have only seen one damaged fender so far. I suppose we must get repairs done faster here than in London," he concluded, as I clutched him back from a crossing where he had not observed the change in a traffic signal. "Why," he asked, ignoring the fact that my action had saved him from adding to the number of damaged automobiles, "do the British call a 'fender' a 'wing' and a 'sidewalk' a 'pavement'?"

Not waiting for any reply to his question, Old Prime continued, "In my search for damaged 'wings' I have been looking at the license numbers and noted a curious coincidence. Each of the last three automobiles had a license number of some letters followed by a three digit number. The sum of the numbers on the first two automobiles equaled the number of the third automobile and the number formed by the last two digits of the number of the third automobile was twice the first digit on the automobile. Further, each digit from 1 to 9 occurred once only. Can you tell me the number on the last automobile?"

38

The Square Peg

WHAT is the maximum size for a square peg which can be inserted in a round hole 2 inches in diameter?

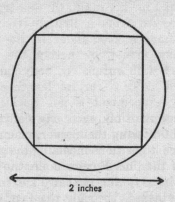

2 inches

39

Alastair's Bicycle

ALASTAIR and his friend, George, decide to go over to George's home which is a mile away. Unfortunately George has no bicycle. They agree that George shall ride Alastair's bicycle part of the way, leave it by the roadside and walk the remainder. Alastair starts walking to George's home at the same time as George sets out on the bicycle. He picks up the bicycle where George had left it and rides the rest of the way. They both reach George's home together. Alastair walks at 4 miles per hour and rides at 12 miles per hour. George is a slower walker and makes only 3 miles per hour but rides at the same speed as Alastair. How far along the route did George leave the bicycle?

40
The Eight Coins

EIGHT dimes, four with heads uppermost and four with tails uppermost, are placed in a row touching each other, thus:

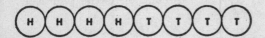

A move consists of taking any two adjacent coins and, without altering their order, placing them in any two vacant positions including the positions at the ends of the line. For example, the first move might consist of taking the third and fourth coins and placing them at the right hand end of the line.

And the next move might consist of moving the two coins in the eighth and ninth positions to the now vacant third and fourth positions.

The problem is to rearrange the coins in four such moves so that heads and tails are arranged alternatively with no gaps.

41
Missing Digits

"Most missing digit problems are quite difficult," remarked Old Prime, "but here is a really easy one to encourage you to take an interest in this class of puzzle.

"The only explicit information is the two decimal points and the zero.

	Line
x·xxx	(1)
xx·x)xx	(2)
xxx	(3)
xxxx	(4)
xxxx	(5)
0	

"We first note that the dividend is a two-digit whole number. Hence the last three digits of line (4) which are brought down from line (2) must all be 0. Now, since the division comes out without any remainder, line (5) must equal the (4), and the last three digits of line (5) are all 0. The last digit, the one after the decimal point, of the divisor must be 5 since otherwise the last two digits of line (5) could not be 0. This means the last digit of line (3) must be 5 or 0. 0 is impossible because this would make the first digit of line (4) 0. Hence the first digit of line (4) and line (5) are 5. We can now proceed to the complete reconstruction."

Can you reconstruct the complete division?

42
Throw It Overboard!

A BOAT floating on a lake has some heavy pieces of iron in its hold. If the iron is thrown overboard, does the level of the lake rise, stay the same, or fall?

43
Mark's Library

MARK has collected quite a mathematical and science library. A number of his books, 22 in fact, are paperback reprints of famous works. Mark's main interest is mathematics and exactly 60 per cent of his books are on various aspects of this subject. There are two books on biology. Of the remainder, two-thirds are on physics and one-third on chemistry. Mark tells me he hopes to increase the size of his library to 50 volumes by next Christmas.

How many books are there in Mark's library?

44
The Fly and the Trains

TWO RAILROAD trains are approaching one another on a single railroad track, each traveling at 30 miles per hour. A fly, traveling at 60 miles per hour, starts from train A, when the two trains are 10 miles apart, and flies until it reaches train B. It turns around without loss of time and flies back

towards train A. Here it again turns around and
flies towards train B. The fly continues to travel
backwards and forwards between the trains,
maintaining its speed of 60 miles per hour and
flying a shorter journey on each successive trip.
Finally the fly is killed when the trains collide.
How far does the fly travel?

45
Dr. Pepper's Puzzle

SOME puzzles can be presented properly only in
verbal form. In setting out in print the following
attractive puzzle due to Dr. Perry Pepper, "tu"
has been used to represent any one of the almost
identical sounds of "to," "two" and "too."

> Add twenty tu tu twenty tu
> And twenty tu as well.
> The answer will depend upon
> The way you choose to spell.

46
Spider and Fly

A ROOM is 16 feet long, 12 feet broad and 8 feet
high. The length of the room runs East and West.
There are no doors or windows at the West end
of the room. A spider on the ceiling of the room,
2 feet from the South wall and 2 feet from the
West wall, sees a fly sleeping on the North wall,

2 feet from the West wall and 1 foot from the floor. If the spider crawls across the ceiling parallel to the West wall and then crawls down the North wall to the fly, he will travel 10 feet across the ceiling and 7 feet down the wall, making 17 feet in all. There is a shorter route the spider can crawl to reach the fly. Can you find it and calculate how long it is?

47
A Game of Bridge

THREE men, Sam, Cam and Laurie, are married to Carrie, Billy and Tina, but not necessarily respectively.

Sam's wife and Billy's husband play Carrie and Tina's husband at bridge. No wife partners her husband and Cam does not play bridge. Who is married to whom?

48
Four or More

"IT WAS Voltaire who said, 'Almost all of human life depends on probabilities,' and I suppose it is true that I earn my living, at least in part, because of my understanding of probabilities," remarked Old Prime. "A young teacher friend of mine came to me in great excitement one day. He had found that two of the pupils in his class had the same birthday. He felt this was an astounding coincidence. I suppose most people, when asked, would give long odds against the chance that with a class of, say, 30 pupils, two pupils would have the same birthday. Actually, if the class has 23 pupils or more, it is more likely than not that two pupils will have the same birthday and, if the teacher continues to record his pupils' birthdays, he will find that common birthdays are quite usual in a class of normal size. The theory of this is not difficult, but the arithmetic is rather tedious. Here is a problem similar in difficulty, but more simple in arithmetic. What is the probability of throwing 4 or more with a single throw of a pair of dice?"

49
The Man, the Boys and the Groceries

A COUNTRY man is walking home from a marketing expedition with his two young boys and a large basket of groceries. They are all tired and the journey is long because they have to go around a large estuary. There is a narrow point where a crossing of part of the estuary will make a great saving in distance. It is near full tide so there is no significant current through the narrows. What is more a small boat is available. However the boat will only take the man and one boy or the man and the groceries. The boys cannot row and cannot be left alone with the groceries, because they may eat the cakes and other attractive foods.

How does the man get the boys and the groceries across?

50
Sharing the Wine

TWO MEN have 8 quarts of wine, which is in an 8-quart container. They have an empty 5-quart jar and an empty 3-quart jar. Assuming the container and the jars hold exactly the amounts specified, and the men have no other means of measuring, how can they divide the wine equally?

51
Living to Seventy

I HAD read somewhere that teachers live longer than attorneys and I asked Old Prime which was the longest lived occupation. "Well," he replied, "that is very difficult to say. If I had to hazard a guess I would suggest bishops. I have never heard of a bishop dying at a young age: they near-ly all live to be seventy, eighty or more." Old Prime refused to be drawn into further discussion of the subject except to add that overweight and longevity rarely went together. However, he posed this problem:

"Relying on the Bible rather than actuarial tables, I expect to live to three score years and ten. At that time the combined ages of my three sons will be twice my age plus 3 years; the ages of two of my sons will be twice the age of the third son plus 2 years; and the age of one of my sons will be the age of another son plus 1 year. All these ages are in exact numbers of years and as you know I do not have twin sons. What will be the sons' ages when I am 70?"

52
The Barber's Shop

A BARBER'S shop is 12 feet wide and has mirrors on both side walls. Looking into the mirror which is 4 feet in front of me, I can see not only my normal reflection but a series of reflections growing smaller and dimmer as they disappear into the distance. Every other image shows my back view. How far does the second image (the first back view) appear to be away?

53
A "Prime" Formula

"THE TROUBLE with prime numbers," said Old Prime one day, "is that they are so irregular. You cannot establish any formula for them, though many have tried. I was presented with this formula a short time ago:

$$x^2 - 3x + 43$$

It works very well. Making some random tests, x = 1 gives 41, x = 3 gives 43, x = 10 gives 113, x = 25 gives 593; all primes. But it did not require any extensive tests to find a value of x which would give a composite number." (A number which can be factorized.) What is a number for which the formula fails?

54
Mix and Match

JOAN buys 3 skirts, 4 blouses and 3 sweaters which she intends to wear in various combinations. The jade green blouse would look unattractive with the olive green skirt but otherwise any combination of the three garments is attractive. How many different, attractive combinations of the three garments can Joan make?

NOT SO EASY

55
Old Prime's Gourmet Club

OLD PRIME fancies himself as a gourmet and he and three of his similarly inclined male friends meet every three months or so at one of their homes for a special gourmet dinner. The host chooses the menu and allocates the preparation of each dish to himself or to one of the other men. The four friends' wives do not help with the preparation of the meal. They just look beautiful and praise their husbands' culinary efforts. The host invites a married couple as guests so there are 10 at the table. The host and hostess sit at the ends of the table with the female guest on the host's right and the male guest on the hostess's right. The seating at the table is alternate man and woman, with no wife next to her husband.

Old Prime was telling me about a recent dinner.

"I found Bob's instructions for Shrimp and Bacon Kebab easy to follow, and both my neighbors at the table, Nancy and Ibby, said it was delicious.

"Frank made a most tasty sauce marinara and described its preparation in detail to Nancy, who was seated next to him.

"Louise had never met the man on her left.

"Alec was, as usual, responsible for the wines.

"The guests were Marty and June."

I know Old Prime's wife is called Billy. How was everyone seated and who is married to whom?

56
The Dispatch Rider

A CONVOY of mechanized troops, 5 miles long, takes 15 minutes to pass a certain point. It takes a dispatch rider 20 minutes to ride from the rear to the front of the moving convoy and to return. How fast does the dispatch rider travel?

57
A Multiplication Sum

IN THE following multiplication sum four of the digits are given, the rest are omitted. The nine digits, 1 to 9, each appear once and only once in the multiplier and the multiplicand.

```
            xxxx
           xxxxx
           ─────
           xxxxx
           xxx2
           xxx8
          xxx0x
         xxxx0
        ──────────
        xxxxxxxxx
```

Can you reconstruct the whole multiplication?

A Prime Number Problem

OLD PRIME was speaking on his favorite subject. "We know so little and so much about prime numbers. A prime is a positive integer which has no divisors other than itself and 1. (1 is not included among the prime numbers.) The sequence of primes—2, 3, 5, 7, 11, 13, 17, 19, etc.—never ends, but primes get less frequent as we progress. There are 168 primes less than 1,000, 135 in the next 1,000 and only 53 in the last 1,000 numbers below 10,000,000. There is no formula for the nth prime, but the number of primes less than n grows closer and closer to $n/\log_e n$ as n gets larger.

"Until recently the largest isolated prime known was $2^{127}-1$, a number of 39 digits. By means of an electronic computer the primality of 2^n-1 has been investigated recently for all values of n up to 2,297, and the largest isolated prime known is now $2^{2281}-1$. Numbers of the form 2^n-1 are known as Mersenne numbers.

"In contrast with the vast feats of calculation involved in establishing the primality of these numbers, here is a simple problem you may like to consider.

"I was looking at the year's results for a certain class of insurance. The tabulation showed the percentage of the premiums absorbed in losses, expenses and profits. The percentages were in exact integers and, of course, added up to 100. I noted that expenses were more than a third but less than a half of the loss payments and that each percentage was a prime number. What were the percentage figures for losses, expenses and profits, respectively?"

59
Insurance Officers

THE PRESIDENT, Actuary, Agency Vice President and Corporate Secretary of a certain insurance company are Mr. Lidstone, Mr. King, Mr. Sprague and Mr. Watson, but not necessarily respectively.

Mr. Sprague served with the President in the First World War. Mr. Watson hopes to be the next President. Mr. Lidstone and the Secretary like to go to the theater together.

Mr. Sprague beats the Actuary at gin rummy. Mr. Lidstone is an artistically minded young man. Mr. Watson never goes to the theater or plays cards. What are the respective names of the company's officers?

60
Cake Eating

TWO BOYS are left to get their own supper while their parents are out at a dinner party. For their dessert there is a circular chocolate cake 20 inches in circumference. The parents had not been explicit in their instructions about the amount of cake the boys should eat, and the boys decide they can consume it all between them. John suggests they should cut slices in turn so that neither has more than his fair share. Christopher agrees and adds the further condition that no slice, measured round the circumference, should be more than two inches or less than one inch. Further the boy who takes the last slice should clean up and wash the dishes. If Christopher, as the eldest, takes the first slice, how should he cut it to avoid washing the dishes?

61
Aptitude Tests

"APTITUDE Tests with multiple choice answers are all the rage nowadays," said Old Prime. "Some of these tests are quite valuable and others are incredibly stupid. They can be helpful in testing mathematical talents, although a student without much talent can study to pass aptitude tests as well as he can study any other subject.

"One form of mathematical test consists of finding the rule in a series and then determining the next term from a choice of five answers. For some reason all the tests of this form I have seen use series which, while following logical rules, are not series which would normally occur to a mathematician. The skilled mathematician will, therefore, probably take appreciably longer than the layman on the first four or five of these he tackles. Since these tests include a time limit that makes it almost impossible to complete the tests, a day's practice will make an enormous difference to most people's scores. Here are some examples similar to those in an actual test. The answer to the first problem is (b)."

							Choice of Answers				
							(a)	(b)	(c)	(d)	(e)
(i)	1	2	1	2	1	2	0	1	2	3	4
(ii)	7	7	7	4	4	4	0	1	2	3	4
(iii)	4	6	12	14	28	30	32	40	60	62	84
(iv)	54	108	36	72	24	48	9	12	15	16	20
(v)	30	5	1	4	12	6	2	4	6	8	10

62
The Golden Ratio

THE golden ratio is considered to have special artistic significance. There are many expressions for it, one of which is the simple continued fraction:

$$1 + \cfrac{1}{1 + \cfrac{1}{1 + \cfrac{1}{1 + \text{etc.}}}}$$

While this has attractive simplicity, it can be expressed in more practical forms.

Can you express the golden ratio (1) in a simple formula; (2) as a decimal?

63
A Network Problem

A NETWORK consists of a number of lines connected together at points. In a closed network all lines end at a point and three or more lines must end at each point. An example of a simple network in two dimensions is shown below.

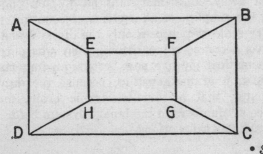

The network has 8 points: A, B, C, D, E, F, G and H. It has 12 lines: AB, BC, CD, DA, AE, BF, CG, DH, EF, FG, GH, HE, and 5 enclosed areas ABFE, AEHD, EFGH, FBCG and HGCD. There is a simple rule connecting the number of points, lines and areas for a network on a plain surface. Can you find the rule?

64
The Binary Scale

"WE USE the scale of ten, the decimal system, in practically all our arithmetic because we were born with ten fingers and thumbs," remarked Old Prime. "Other scales are just as practical if not more so. The scale of twelve, or duodecimal scale, is particularly attractive because 12 is divisible by 2, 3, 4 and 6 while 10 is divisible by 2 and 5 only. Vestiges of the use of this scale still exist in our measures. For example, 12 inches make a foot and 12 x 12 is a gross. But we are wedded to the decimal system and it is time these anachronisms were swept away. Mathematicians have often played with the simplest of all systems of counting, the binary scale, which uses only the digits 0 and 1. As has occurred often before, what was once a mathematical toy has now become an important application of mathematics, because the digital computer, that moronic electronic brain, must reduce all numbers to the binary system before it can make its calculations.

"The binary scale is best understood by some examples:

Decimal Scale	Binary Scale
1	1
2	10
3	11
4	100
5	101
8	1,000
16	10,000
18	10,010 etc.

"You will note that a 1 in the nth position from the right in a binary scale number is equal to 2^{n-1} just as 1 in the nth position from the right in a decimal scale number is equal to 10^{n-1}."

What is the representation in the binary scale of the number represented by 101 in the decimal scale?

65
The Two Ladders

TWO TWENTY-FOOT ladders are leaning next to each other against the side of a house. Obviously they are not being used because one of them is at such a low angle that it would be unsafe to climb; in fact, a rock is stopping it from slipping to the ground. The top of one ladder touches the house at 16 feet above the ground, the top of the other touches at 12 feet. Since the ladders are side by side, there is a point where the left side of one ladder touches the right side of the other. If the ladders do not sag, how high is this point above the ground?

66
Choosing the Weights

A STORE has a large supply of 1 lb., 3 lb., 9 lb. and 27 lb. weights, but no weights of other amounts. These weights are sold at 25 cents per pound regardless of size. $10.00 will, therefore, buy 40 lbs. of weights and a man wishes to limit his purchase to this sum. In how many different ways can he choose the 40 lbs. of weights to weigh every integral number of pounds from 1 lb. to 40 lbs. on a balance scales in which weights can be placed in either pan with the condition that each weighing can be made in one way only? For example, if the man buys three or more 1 lb. weights he cannot buy a 3 lb. weight, since he could weigh 3 lbs. either with three 1 lb. weights or with one 3 lb. weight thus giving him two ways of weighing 3 lbs.

67
The Blue Egg

OLD PRIME was telling me about the annual competition between the Branch Offices of his company for a trophy affectionately known as the "Blue Egg." "Points 0, 1, 2, 3, 4 or 5, are awarded for achievement in each of four separate fields: Life Insurance, Fire Insurance, Casualty Insurance and Office Efficiency. Last year the results were a great surprise as three Branch Offices, Philadelphia, Boston and New Orleans, all tied for first place. Philadelphia's success was most surprising because their points for Casualty Insurance were the lowest of any Branch Office. Boston did better in both Fire and Casualty than in either Life or Efficiency. New Orleans had the same points for Life as Boston had Efficiency, and Philadelphia and New Orleans had identical points for Efficiency.

"A curious feature of the results was that the points scored in the four fields of endeavor by each of the winning offices, when arranged in order of increasing size, produced a different four-digit number for each office and every possible such number, consistent with the total score, occurred. What were the scores of the three leading offices in each field?"

68
The Cigarette Box

WHAT is the maximum number of cigarettes ⅜ inch in diameter which can be placed in a box, 6 inches long and 3 inches deep, so that no part of any cigarette is above the level of the top of the box? The box is as broad as the cigarettes are long.

69
The Goat in the Field

A SQUARE shack 30 feet by 30 feet is in the middle of an open field. A goat is tethered to one corner of the shack, by a chain 60 feet long. She cannot get under the shack but can graze anywhere else she can reach on her chain. What is the area of the portion of the field she can graze?

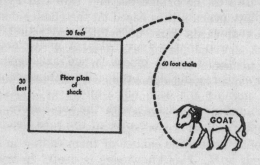

70
School Reports

MARK has three school reports in a year. He is studying 5 subjects and is graded A, B, C, D or E in each subject. In order to encourage greater application, his father promised to pay Mark $1.50 for each A, $1.05 for each B, 75¢ for each C and 15¢ for each D. Of course no payment is made for an E. In a certain year Mark managed to avoid any E's and received the same total payment for the results of each of his three reports, although the distribution of A's, B's, C's and D's was different each time. Further, the total amount he received in the year was an even number of dimes. How much did he receive?

71
Old Prime on Bridge

"A KNOWLEDGE of probability can be of considerable help to the bridge player," said Old Prime, "but any probabilities based on the chance distribution of cards must be modified to reflect the knowledge the player has developed concerning his opponents' hands. With two cards out against you and no knowledge of your opponents' hands, the chance that both cards will fall in one round is $\frac{1}{2}$. With three cards out against you and a similar lack of knowledge concerning your opponents' hands, the chance of them falling in two rounds is $\frac{3}{4}$. This knowledge is useful in trying to choose between a finesse and playing for cards to drop.

"You occasionally read in the paper that a perfect hand, 13 cards of one suit, has been dealt in actual play. If the cards are properly shuffled, one such hand should occur less than once in a hundred thousand million games (actually 1 in 158,753,389,900). If we assume a million players have played 20 hands per sitting, 20 sittings a year for 150 years, 60,000,000,000 hands would have been played. The occurrence of one or even two perfect hands in this number would be credible, but the number of cases reported are much too frequent for proper shuffling of hands. To have all four hands perfect gets us into such astronomical figures (the actual probability is 1 in 2,235,197,406,895,366,368,301,560,000) that we may be sure that such a deal could occur after complete shuffling only once in many millions of years.

"A yarborough is a hand of cards which holds

no honors (A, K, Q, J or 10) and gets its name from an Earl of Yarborough who bet 1,000 to 1 against such a hand being dealt. The actual odds are 1,827 to 1.

"With four cards out against you what is the chance they are divided 2 and 2 and will, therefore, fall in 2 rounds?"

72
Jigsaw Squares

"A SQUARE may be subdivided readily into a number of smaller squares or, to put it another way, a number of squares may be considered pieces of a jigsaw puzzle making up a larger square," said Old Prime.

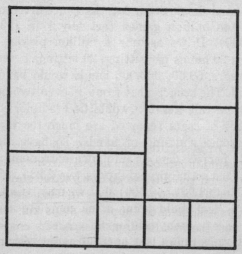

"But if we add the condition that no two of the smaller squares making up the larger square can be the same size, we have a problem of outstanding difficulty which has been solved only quite recently.

"Here is a similar but much easier problem. Can you arrange 9 square pieces, with sides measuring 1, 4, 7, 8, 9, 10, 14, 15 and 18 inches, so as to form a single rectangle?"

73
The Christmas Gifts

ONE Christmas a rich grandfather gave each of his grandsons as many dollars as he had grandsons, and each of his granddaughters as many dollars as he had granddaughters. These gifts cost in total $841. How many grandchildren were there?

74
In the Middle

"MY STUDY is slightly below the level of the rest of the ground floor of our house," remarked Old Prime, "and you have to go down three steps to it. When we have young children visiting the house, I always ask them to count the steps and then to point out the middle step. It is not as easy as it sounds. Just take a look at the drawing overleaf.

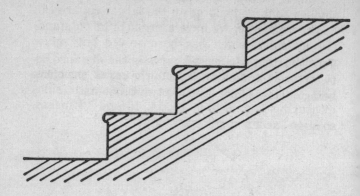

"The middle of something is really quite a complicated notion," continued Old Prime, "my statistical friends have three different terms for the middle of a set of observations—the mean, the mode and the median—all meaning something different, and the middle of certain solid bodies (for example, a horseshoe) is not inside the solid at all. Here is a little problem which you may find interesting:

"If you take a long strip of paper—the gummed paper often used for securing parcels is most suitable—and cut it in half down the middle, you get two equal strips the same length but half the original breadth. Now, stick the two ends of the paper together to form a loop before cutting the paper. In this case you will, of course, get two loops each the same size as the original loop but half as wide. Suppose, before you stick the two ends together, you give one end of the strip half a turn, so that the gummed side of one end is stuck to the gummed side of the other end. What is now the result of cutting the loop down the middle?"

75
Curves of Equal Breadth

THE BREADTH of a closed curve is the distance between two parallel tangents to the curve, the curve being contained between the two tangents.

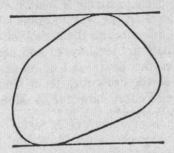

As the curve is orientated in respect to the direction of the tangents, the breadth of the curve will normally vary. A circle has the property that its breadth is constant (equal to the diameter). It is this property which makes a set of rollers of equal circular cross section suitable for moving a heavy, flat-based body over a level floor.

Can you discover a curve, other than a circle, which has the same breadth, however orientated?

76
The Woltons

"THE ENGLISH countryside, with its little hills and dales and fascinating village names, and the English bicycle, which is such a pleasure to ride, lend themselves to the construction of puzzles," said Old Prime.

"Monk's Wolton is due north and Bishop's Wolton is due east of Great Wolton, and the road to each from Great Wolton is straight.

"Starting from Great Wolton it takes me the same time to bicycle to Monk's Wolton and back as it does to bicycle to Bishop's Wolton and back, but then it is level all the way to Monk's Wolton and a steady uphill climb to Bishop's Wolton. Uphill I bicycle at half my level speed and downhill I bicycle half as fast again as I do on the level. If it is 5 miles as the crow flies from Monk's Wolton to Bishop's Wolton, how far is Monk's Wolton from Great Wolton?"

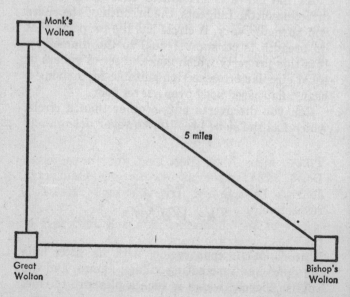

77
Old Prime's Marbles

"CHILDREN do not play with marbles any more," said Old Prime. "They seem no longer content with such simple toys, but when I was young there were not the marvelous plastic models to build there are today. Which makes a child more dextrous, marbles or plastic models? Probably the latter. I came across a bag of marbles in the attic and when some children were in the house one wet day I set them to play Ring-taw and those other old games. Each child won a different number of games and the total number of games won by the boys equaled the total number won by the two girls. As a memento of the occasion, I gave each child a present of marbles, equal to the square of the number of games he or she had won. In total, the boys received as many marbles as the girls, and I gave away all my marbles, which numbered less than 100. How many marbles did I have?"

78
Three Families

THREE men, Alex, Bert and Joe, have wives, Doris, Effie and Frances, and one child each, Jeffrey, Horace and Iris, but not necessarily respectively.

Two of the children, Effie's and Joe's, are on the school wrestling team.

Alex's son is not Jeffrey.

Bert's wife is not Frances.

Who is whose wife and whose child?

The Measurement of Time

OLD PRIME was speaking on the passage of time. "Some hours drag by and others are gone in a flash. Certainly in our appreciation of the passage of time there is no such regularity as the ticking clock suggests. However, there does seem to be a general speeding up of our sense of the passage of time as we grow older. A friend of mine made this interesting suggestion. Our mind can be considered schematically as a thread of fixed length on which are placed the beads of experience. The beads are equally spaced along the thread so that, as we have more and more experiences, they are clustered closer and closer together. Our sense of the passage of time corresponds to the space the experience passed through occupies on the thread. Of course, our mind is not as simple as this schematic plan suggests; but this idea leads to the thought that the passage of a certain event which takes, let us say an hour at age 20, will seem to take half as long ($\frac{20}{40} \times 1$ hour) at age 40 and one-third the time ($\frac{20}{60} \times 1$ hour) at age 60, which is fairly close, I believe, to actual experience.

"If it is assumed that this law really holds, at what age does a period of two hours give the same impression of the passage of time as one hour at age 20 plus one hour at age 60?"

The Chain of Weights

BOBBY had built a pair of scales with his Erector set and was looking for some suitable weights to use with them. He found an old copper chain with 23 links. These links would make excellent weights if he could separate the chain into its links. To cut open 23 links was no small task, so he went to consult Old Prime, who lived nearby.

"Well," said Old Prime, "this is not such a big job as you think. First, you do not need to cut the first and last links because they will fall off if you cut all the others. In fact you can separate the chain into all its links by cutting every even-numbered link. This would mean only eleven cuts. Of course, some of the links will be cut and some not, but your scales are not sufficiently accurate to detect the slight difference in weight between the two. But, Bobby, you need not cut the chain into all its links. You do not need 23 one-link weights. It would be more convenient to have some two-link, three-link or larger weights. Now here is a chance to test your mathematics. What is the fewest number of links which must be cut so that you can weigh any number of links from 1 to 23 (using only one pan of the scales for weights), and which links should be cut?"

Honeycomb Tiling

A ROOM is paved with small hexagonal tiles which are two inches across from the middle of one side to the middle of the opposite side. They are fastened down with cement which shows between the tiles. There is ⅕th of an inch of cement between the side of one tile and the side of any adjoining tile. What percentage of the floor covering is cement?

82
Eulerian Square

"Do you know what an Eulerian Square is?" my friend Old Prime asked one day. When I admitted my ignorance he went on to explain that the Eulerian, or Greco-Latin, square was the combination of two Latin squares, thus:

a	b	c
b	c	a
c	a	b

$+$

α	β	ν
ν	α	β
β	ν	α

$=$

$a\alpha$	$b\beta$	$c\nu$
$b\nu$	$c\alpha$	$a\beta$
$c\beta$	$a\nu$	$b\alpha$

In the final square each letter appears once and only once in each line and column and each Latin letter combines once and only once with each Greek letter. "These squares are used," explained Old Prime, "in planning test planting in agricultural research so as to minimize the effects on the tests of stratified soil variations. Such squares have been known for many years where the number of rows (and columns) are an odd number or a multiple of 4, but it was conjectured by the mathematician Euler that for 6, 10 and other 'uneven even' numbers the square could not be constructed. It was only in 1958 that a solution was found for a square of order 10 and other larger 'uneven even' numbers. No solution exists for order 6."

A puzzle based on the Eulerian Square is to arrange a pack of 16 playing cards consisting of all the Aces, Kings, Queens and Jacks in a four by four square so that each suit and each rank appears once and only once in each row, column and diagonal.

83
Angles on a Cube

DIAGONALS, BD and GD in the illustration, are drawn on each of two adjoining faces of a cube, so that they meet at one of the corners of the cube.

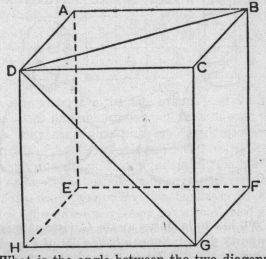

What is the angle between the two diagonals?

84
The Hymn Board

THE HYMNAL used in a certain church contains 680 hymns. There are three hymns at each service and the hymns are indicated on a hymn board which uses cards showing one of the digits 0 to 9. What is the minimum number of cards needed to show any combination of three hymn numbers? How many fewer cards are needed if the same card can be used for 9 as for 6 by turning it upside down?

85
A Party Game

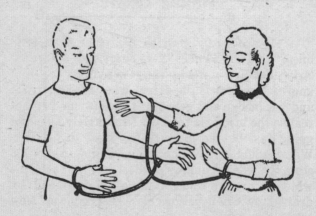

"IF YOU like to brighten up the Christmas season with party games, you can have a lot of fun with this one," said Old Prime. "A volunteer is asked to hold out his hands and the two ends of a piece of strong string, about 3 or 4 feet long, are securely tied, one round each of his wrists. A second volunteer has her wrists similarly tied but, before the second end of her string is tied round her wrist, it is looped through the string joining the wrists of the first volunteer.

"The two volunteers are then asked to disentangle themselves without untying or cutting either string. Usually a great deal of stepping through the loops and similar maneuvers take place without any progress to the desired goal. How can the players separate themselves from each other?"

86
Turnpike Driving

"THERE are many puzzles concerning automobiles," said Old Prime. "Two short ones I particularly like are unfortunately becoming too well known. The first is the driver who takes his truck under a bridge and gets stuck because he does not realize the bridge is too low. Fortunately he is not going fast but he is stuck too tight to get-free. What should he do? The second is the driver who stupidly, when changing a wheel, lets the four nuts which secure the wheel in place roll down a street drain. How can he secure his wheel in place? Now try this long one.

"Mileage on the Thru-State Turnpike is measured from the Eastern terminal. Driver A enters the turnpike at the Centerville entrance, which is at the 65-mile marker, and drives east. After he has traveled 5 miles and is at the 60-mile marker, he overtakes a man operating a white-line painting machine who is traveling east at 5 miles per hour. At the 35-mile marker he passes his friend B, whose distinctive car he happens to spot, driving west. The time he notes is 12:20 p.m. At the 25-mile marker he passes a grass cutter traveling west at 10 miles per hour. A later learns that B overtook the grass cutter at the 21-mile marker and passed the white-line painter at the 56-mile marker. Assuming A, B, the painter and the grass cutter all travel at constant speeds, at what time did A enter the turnpike?"

87
Population Growth

"THE CONTINUED growth of the population of the world is a most serious problem which will not be solved by sending people in rockets to the moon," remarked Old Prime one evening. "While we usually connect the problem of population growth with Malthus, who published his 'Essay on Population' in 1798, I came across in an old actuarial journal an amusing essay on the same subject by an English scientist, Sir William Petty, which was published about one hundred years earlier. Sir William calculated that 20 thousand million people had died between the Flood and 1692 and that all these people could have been buried on one-fifth part of the surface of Ireland without putting two bodies in any one grave.

"I don't know why Sir William picked on Ireland and do not believe there can be any real connection between his proposal and the reduction in the population of Ireland which has taken place over the last 100 years."

Old Prime had clearly been studying the population problem because he went on to say, "Do you realize that over one-quarter of a million children are born each day. Of course, people die too, but each year the world population increases by about 50 million—the equivalent of adding an entire nation the size of France.

"The idea of growth provides many interesting mathematical problems. There is the well-known one of the amoeba which grows by dividing itself. Let us assume it doubles its number every day. If it takes 50 days to cover completely the surface of a tank with the amoebae, how long does it take to cover half the surface? The answer is, of course, 49 days.

"Many people have difficulties with the conception of growth. Which is the faster rate of growth, 1 per cent a week or 60 per cent a year?"

88

A Dice Game

"THERE is a game we sometimes play," said Old Prime, "which involves 5 dice. It is a round game for any number of players. The player whose turn it is throws the 5 dice simultaneously and can re-throw subject to the rules I am going to describe. Each player aims to have the greatest possible total on his 5 dice. With a score of 24 he receives and pays out nothing. For each point over 24 he receives one chip from each other player; for each point below 24 he pays one chip to each other player. The re-throw rules are as follows: After each throw or re-throw one or more of the dice just thrown must be declared dead and cannot be re-thrown. All dice not declared dead must be immediately re-thrown. For example, I throw:

$$6.5.4.1.1$$

"I declare 6 . 5 dead and re-throw the three dice showing 4 . 1 . 1. These now turn up 5 . 5 . 3. I declare the two additional 5's dead and re-throw the remaining die which now turns up a 1. This must be declared dead by the rules and my total score is $6 + 5 + 5 + 5 + 1 = 22$. I pay everyone 2 chips. If I had declared all the dice dead after the second throw my score would have been 24.

"With two dice declared dead, I throw:

(1) 6.5.4
(2) 6.5.3
(3) 6.4.4

"How many dice should I re-throw in each case to have the best scoring expectation?"

Of Pigs and Dogs

"THERE is a very fascinating problem involving a farmer and a pig," said Old Prime. "The pig enters a square field at a gate in the southeast corner and runs directly towards the northeast corner at constant speed. The farmer, who runs twice as fast as the pig, enters the field at the southwest corner at the same time as the pig enters the field and chases the pig. The farmer although a fast runner is not very bright and runs directly towards the pig, making no attempt to head the pig off. As the pig moves up the field, the farmer continually alters his direction so he is always running directly towards the pig. How far up the edge of the field does the pig get before the farmer overtakes him?

"The answer," said Old Prime, "is two-thirds of the way to the northeast corner. Unfortunately I have not been able to find a solution which does not involve calculus. However, here is a very similar puzzle that can be solved without any advanced mathematics.

"Four dogs, A, B, C and D, enter a square field simultaneously at the NE, SE, SW and NW corners respectively. All dogs run at the same speed and dog A chases dog B, dog B chases dog C, dog C chases dog D and dog D chases dog A. Like the farmer they are not very bright and each always runs directly towards the dog it is chasing. Obviously the dogs will spiral into the center of the field. If the sides of the field are 200 yards, how far will each dog run before they all meet in the center?"

90
Over the Hill

THE MOST direct route from Little Puddle to Great Puddle is over the hill. Unfortunately I cannot ride my bicycle up the hill, so I have to push it, but I can free-wheel all the way down the other side. The top of the hill is exactly half way. I walk, pushing my bicycle, at 3 miles per hour and I ride down at twice my normal level speed. There is a level road which goes around the hill which is 7 miles longer but actually it saves me 15 minutes.

If I take the level road more easily and bicycle at five-sixths of my normal speed, the two routes take the same time.

How long does it take me to walk to the top of the hill?

91
Drawing an Ellipse

"IF A PARABOLA is a rectangular hyperbola, prove that it is also an equiangular spiral." I was looking over Old Prime's shoulder at a problem he was studying. "That is sheer nonsense. How can a parabola be a hyperbola?" "The problem is real enough although the curve involved is imaginary," replied Old Prime. "The problem was set by my old teacher, Professor Hardy. If I tell you the curve touches the line at infinity at one of the circular points, I am sure it will be quite clear to you.

But, here is a problem which you will find more practical:

"The ellipse, the parabola and the hyperbola are all known as conic sections because they are obtained by cutting a right circular cone by a plane. If your son wants to draw an ellipse for some mathematical drawing, how can he do it accurately with a pencil and some simple aids he can find round the house?"

92
Crossing the Desert

AN EXPLORER sets out to cross a desert 1,150 miles wide in a truck which travels 10 miles to the gallon of gasoline. With other equipment the truck can carry only 75 gallons (including what is in its tank). There are no gasoline supplies in the desert but gasoline can be deposited in safety by the truck along the route. How does the truck cross the desert using the minimum amount of gasoline? The necessity of taking extra gasoline in case of losing the way, etc., is to be ignored.

93
Three Sevens

WITH exactly three 4's and various mathematical symbols we can express a large assortment of numbers. For example:

$$\frac{\sqrt{4} + \sqrt{4}}{4} = 1$$

$$\frac{4}{4} \sqrt{4} = 2$$

$$4 + \frac{4}{4} = 5$$

$$\frac{44}{4} = 11$$

$$\frac{4 + 4}{.4} = 20, \text{etc.}$$

In this manner, can you express 4 in terms of three 7's?

94
The Missing Dollar

OLD PRIME was talking about gambling. "I enjoy gambling in a modest way, but I never really expect to win. In fact I find the theory of gambling, with all its subtle paradoxes, more interesting than the actual practice of the sport.

"If you stake a fixed percentage of your fortune on an even chance a number of times, adjusting your stake to the revised level after each play, and if you win exactly as many times as you lose, you will always have less money after playing than you had when you started. To illustrate this surprising fact, suppose you start with $100 and stake 10 per cent of your fortune each time. If you play but two games, winning one and losing one, you will end up with $99. Your first bet will be $10. If you win you then have $110. You stake $11 on the second game, which you lose, leaving $99. If you lose the first game you have $90. You stake $9 on the second game and win, bringing your total to $99 as before."

Old Prime went on, "If you invest a fixed sum of money in a certain stock on the first of each month, and at the end of the year, or any other period, the price of the stock is equal to its average price on the dates of purchase, you will find you own more stock than if you had made your whole investment at one time at the average price."

Can you reconcile the loss of $1, in the example of betting a fixed percentage of your fortune, with the fact that the probability of winning and losing should be equally likely?

95
A Mistake in Surveying

A MAN, surveying a farm, finds that the farm house and a certain barn, 250 yards to the south of the farm house, are marked on a previous survey. He finds that a certain tree, to the west of the line joining the barn and farm house, is 200 yards from the farm house and 150 yards from the barn.

In making his notes the surveyor interchanges these two distances and records the tree as being 150 yards from the farm house and 200 yards from the barn. What is the distance from the true position of the tree and the position recorded?

96
Getting the Goat

TWO BROTHERS are equal partners in a dairy farm.
They decide to split up and to change to raising
lambs. They sell each of their cows for as many
dollars as they have cows. Lambs cost $10 apiece.
After buying as many lambs as they can with the
money they received from the sale of the cows,
they have a few dollars left over with which they
buy a kid goat. They now find they have purchased
an even number of animals so dividing the animals
between them presents no problem. However, the
brother who gets the goat must receive a sum of
money from the brother who gets all lambs to
equalize the values. How much should he receive?

97
The Rhombicosidodecahedron

"DO YOU realize," said Old Prime, "that mathematicians use at times longer and more frightening
words than doctors? I bet you do not know what a
Rhomb-icosi-dodeca-hedron is. Well, it is one of
the Archimedian solids; you might almost call it
a sphere with knobs on! It is a symmetrical solid
body with plane faces, each of which is a regular
polygon (an equilateral triangle, a square, and so
on). When looked at from any vertex you see the
same arrangement of faces. A cube has 8 vertices
(corners) and looked at from any one of these you
see three square faces meeting at their corners.

With a Rhombicosidodecahedron, four faces meet at each vertex—a square, a pentagon, another square and a triangle. The two squares which meet at each vertex are separated by a pentagon on one side and a triangle on the other. This information defines the solid completely. But to help you visualize it, I will add that each pentagon face is surrounded by 5 square faces, each triangular face is surrounded by 3 square faces and each square face is surrounded by two pentagon faces and two triangular faces arranged alternately. How many vertices and how many faces has a Rhombicosidodecahedron?"

Here is an illustration of a part of the surface of a Rhombicosidodecahedron.

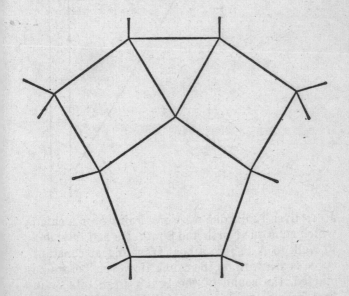

The Canal Boat

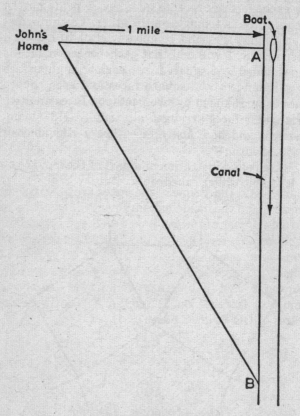

JOHN lives 1 mile due west of a Point A on a canal which runs due North and South. He had intended to walk to A to join a boat traveling at constant speed southward on the canal. However, before he started, the sound of the boat's siren told John that he was unlikely to catch the boat at A. He therefore walked in a straight line across the flats to a point B which he hoped to reach in time to catch the boat. He can join the boat at any point on the bank of the canal provided he reaches it in time to signal to the boat to draw in. If John walks at half the speed of the boat, how far South of A is the point B if John is to have the maximum chance of catching the boat?

99
Old Prime's Boxes

"I HAVE made four boxes each in the shape of a cube," said Old Prime. "The boxes are all different in size, and the inside measurements of each are an exact number of inches. Boxes A, B and C together hold exactly as much as Box D. If I had made all three dimensions of Box B twice as large and all the three dimensions of Box C two inches greater, Boxes A and B together would hold exactly as much as Boxes C and D together." What were the sizes of Old Prime's boxes?

100
The Church Tower

OUR CHURCH tower is square and has a pinnacle on each corner. Driving one day along a straight road in the neighborhood I noticed that the two pinnacles (the N.E. and S.E.) were in line. I set my trip mileage at zero and drove on. I noted that after 1½ miles two pinnacles (the N.W. and S.E.) were in line, and at 3½ miles two pinnacles (the S.W. and S.E.) were again in line. How far was I then from the church?

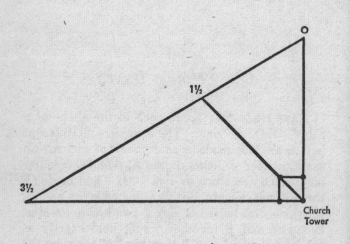

1½

3½

Church
Tower

101
What, No Digits?

THE FOLLOWING long division sum has an x for each digit. The divisor and the dividend are both two-digit integers. The quotient is a single integer followed by an 8-figure recurring decimal. Can you reconstruct the long division sum?

```
          ẋ.xxxxxxxẋ
        _____
   xx) xx
       xx
       ___
       xxx
        xx
        ___
        xxx
        xxx
        ____
         xxx
         xxx
         ____
          xxx
          xxx
          ____
           xxx
           xxx
           ____
            xxx
            xxx
            ____
             xxx
             xxx
             ____
              xxx
```

102
The Twelve Coins

TWELVE coins are identical in appearance, but one of them differs from the rest in weight.

Given only a pair of scales, determine in three weighings which is the odd coin and whether it is lighter or heavier than the rest.

103
The Round Hole

IT IS very easy to determine the theoretical, maximum size of a round hole drilled in a square, flat piece of wood.

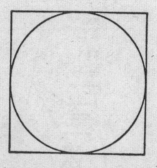

If the wood is 2 inches square, the diameter of the round hole will be 2 inches. In practice the diameter must be somewhat less because, after a 2 inch hole has been cut away, the ring remaining will fall into four separate pieces.

What is the maximum size for a round cylindrical hole drilled through a cube with 2 inch sides? As in the case of the square of wood the hole must go through the cube so that it is completely surrounded by the remains of the cube. Since we do not know how thin wood can be cut before it collapses the size required is the theoretical maximum. When the theoretical maximum hole is cut out, into how many pieces would the ring that remains fall?

For Those Who Like Geometry

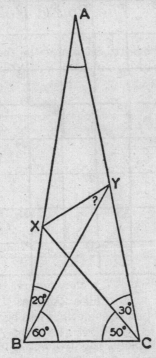

$\widehat{ABY} = 20°$, $\widehat{ACX} = 30°$, $\widehat{XCB} = 50°$ and $\widehat{YBC} = 60°$.

What is the value of $\widehat{XYB}$?

Old Prime's Crossnumber Puzzle

Clues—Across

1. A multiple of this number is obtained by removing the first digit and placing it after the last digit.
7. The year in the twentieth century when Easter is earliest.
11. Divisible by 7, 11 and 13.
12. Multiple of 30 Down.
13. When added to 16 Across is equal to the sum of 23 Down and 25 Down.
14. See 26 Across.
15. A multiple of 9.

16. See 13 Across.
17. This number has the same first and last digits.
18. A multiple of 3.
19. Ten times 31 Across plus five times 13 Across.
21. Factorial 9.
24. Multiple of 28 Across.
26. Sum of 3 Down and 14 Across.
27. See 8 Down.
28. See 24 Across.
29. See 4 Down.
31. See 19 Across.
32. Equal to 22 Down.
33. $10^5 \times \pi$ to the nearest integer.

Clues—Down

1. The cube of a prime number.
2. A multiple of 17 Across.
3. A multiple of 7.
4. Sum of twice 21 Across and 29 Across.
5. See 10 Down.
6. This number is equal to the sum of the cubes of its digits.
7. A cube number.
8. The sum of 15 Across and 27 Across.
9. See 20 Down.
10. A multiple of 5 Down.
19. A square number.
20. Ten times 9 Down plus 1.
22. Equal to 32 Across.
23. See 13 Across.
25. See 13 Across.
30. Factor of 12 Across.

SOLUTIONS

1
But Me No Butts

FIVE. He first makes four cigarettes and smokes them. He then makes an additional cigarette from the butts of these four.

2
Sunday Service

90. THERE are 9 rows of pews.

3
Fence Me In

$105.00. THERE are 11 posts.

4
Milliner's Problem

50¢.

5
The Light That Failed

3 STOCKINGS.

6
Watered Milk

SINCE the two pitchers contain equal quantities of
liquid at the beginning and at the end of the interchanges, the amount of milk in pitcher A must
exactly equal the amount of water in pitcher B.

7
Cafe au lait

THE GREATER the temperature difference between
the liquid and the surrounding air, the faster will
heat be lost. Hence, the cup to which the cream is
added later will lose heat faster and reach drinking temperature first.

8
As the Cog Moves

TWO COMPLETE turns. The problem can be tested
using quarters for cog wheels.

9
The Rains Came

ONE INCH.

10
High Tide

2 RUNGS.

11
The Christmas Gifts

JOAN.

12
High Noon

33 SECONDS. It is the interval between the strokes which takes up the time.

13
Scaled to Weigh

(1) 1, 2, 4, 8, 16, 32 lbs. = 6 weights.
(2) 1, 3, 9, 27 lbs.   = 4 weights.

14
Snail's Pace

IN 27 days and nights the snail will be 3 feet below the top of the well and it climbs out at the end of the 28th day.

15
On the Shelf

1½ INCHES. The bookworm travels through the pages of the second volume only.

16
Housing Problem

HE LOCATED the site of the house at the North Pole.

17
No Radar Trap

THE TRAIN is already about to leave the station and I cannot catch it.

18
Round and Round She Goes

JUST over 3 inches.

19
All Aboard

9 TRAINS.

20
Pound for Pound

THE WEIGHT will rise.

21
Around the World

YOU WOULD cross the date line on your journey and arrive in London 24 hours after you set out.

22
Transmutation

LEAD. Gold is measured in troy weight.
(Troy)   = 12 ozs. (Troy) = 5,760 grains 1 lb.
(Avoirdupois) = 16 ozs.   = 7,000 grains 1 lb.

23
Family Names

DR. LESLIE BROWN is Dr. James Brown's daughter.

24
Rocket to Mars

13,000 MILES and 22 feet.

25
Happy Birthday

JOHN was born just before midnight on February 28th. James was born in the early hours of the morning of February 29th.

26
Mopping Up

7 MONTHS.

27
Mary's Little Lambs

MARY had 14 lambs; Laura had 10 lambs.

28
Tracing a Figure

START at the mid point of the top or the bottom line and the problem is easy to solve.

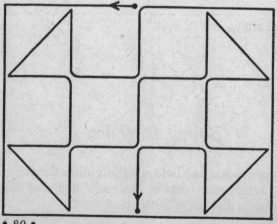

29
My Age

Let x be my age.
Let my son be t years younger, so he is now x − t.
When he is my age (x), I will be x + t.
Hence
$x + t = 5(x − t)$
$x + t = 5x − 5t$
$6t = 4x$
Thus: $t/2 = x/3$
When our joint ages are 50, my age will be 25 + t/2 and my son's age 25 − t/2.
Hence $\frac{1}{2}x = 25 − t/2$ or $x = 50 − t$
Since $3t = 2x$, $3x = 150 − 2x$ or $x = 30$.
I am 30 years old. My son is 10 years old.

30
The Little Orchard

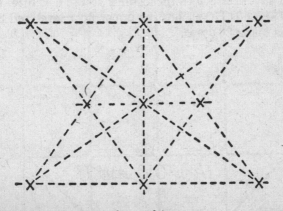

OLD PRIME had ten lines of trees.

31
Colored Cubes

IF WE paint the top face with a particular color, say red, the bottom color can be selected in 5 ways and the four remaining colors can be arranged round the sides in 6 different ways, making 30 fundamentally different cubes.

32
The Escalator

20 STEPS.

In two seconds Old Prime walks up 2 steps and the escalator takes him up an additional step, so he advances 3×8 inches or 2 feet. Therefore, in 20 seconds he reaches the upper floor level and he has taken 20 steps.

33
How Old Am I?

I AM 40 and John is 30.

34
Who is the Architect?

JOAN cannot be the art critic or architect. The aviator must be a man, so Joan must be the acrobat. Hence, Jane, the only other woman, must be the art critic. John cannot be the aviator, who is happily married, so he must be the architect.

35
Chessboard Squares

IF THE small squares have 1-inch sides, there are $8^2 = 64$ 1-inch squares; $7^2 = 49$ 2-inch squares, etc., down to 1 8-inch square. The total number is 204.

36
A Pile of Paper

THE PILE is more than 100,000 inches high. In fact, it is over 10 million inches (more than 100 miles) high, and will, of course, topple over long before completed.

37
The Three Automobile Numbers

THE FIRST digit of the number of the last automobile must be greater than 5, so as to give a two-digit number which does not contain 0 when multiplied by 2. With 612, 714, 816 and 918 as the only possibilities, simple trial or casting out the nines shows that the answer must be 918. Various alternatives are available for the other two numbers. One example is 243 + 675 = 918.

38
The Square Peg

$\sqrt{2}$ = 1.414 inches square.

39
Alastair's Bicycle

3/5THS of a mile.

40
The Eight Coins

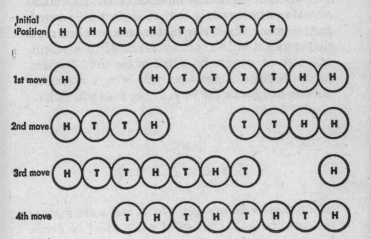

Initial Position: H H H H T T T T

1st move: H ⟶ H T T T T H H

2nd move: H T T H ⟶ T T H H

3rd move: H T T H T H T ⟶ H

4th move: T H T H T H T H

41
Missing Digits

```
            1.008
62.5 ) 6 3
       625
       ────
       5000
       5000
       ────
          0
```

42
Throw It Overboard!

THE INITIAL displacement of the boat is a volume of water whose weight is that of the boat (including the iron). By throwing the iron overboard the displacement of the boat is decreased by a volume of water whose weight is that of the iron. The iron at the bottom of the lake will occupy a smaller volume and hence the level of the lake will fall.

43
Mark's Library

SINCE exactly 60 per cent of the books are mathematical, the total number of books must be divisible by 5. From the other data, the total number must then be 25, 30, 35, 40 or 45 and the number of physics and chemistry books will be 8, 10, 12, 14 or 16. Since the number of physics and chemistry books must total a multiple of 3, Mark must have 35 books.

44
The Fly and the Trains

THE TRAINS are approaching each other at 60 miles per hour and will collide after 10 minutes. Since the fly travels at 60 miles per hour, it will travel 10 miles in this 10 minutes. The distance traveled by the fly is 10 miles.

45
Dr. Pepper's Puzzle

AMONG the many possible solutions, the following are typical:

$$22 + 22 + 22 \quad = \quad 66$$
$$22 + 222 + 20, \text{too} = \quad 262$$
$$22,222 + 22 \quad = 22,244$$

It is difficult to determine the total number of solutions because some argument will occur whether some interpretations are acceptable.

46
Spider and Fly

THE SPIDER can reach the fly by crawling 15 feet if he chooses a route across the West wall. To determine the route we consider the room to be like a cardboard box cut open along the line joining the North wall and ceiling so that the pieces representing the North wall, the West wall and the ceiling can be laid out flat

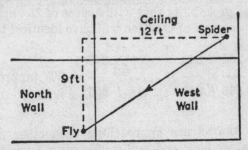

The route taken by the spider is now a straight line and its length is

$$\sqrt{12^2 + 9^2} = 15 \text{ feet}$$

47
A Game of Bridge

CARRIE is married to Cam, Tina is married to Sam and Billy is married to Laurie.

48
Four or More

EACH die can be thrown in six different ways, and hence two dice can be thrown in $6 \times 6 = 36$ ways.

Two can be thrown in one way only, $1 + 1$; three can be thrown in two ways, $1 + 2$ or $2 + 1$.

Hence two or three can be thrown in 3 ways and the probability of throwing 4 or more is

$$1 - \frac{3}{36} = \frac{11}{12}$$

The probability that with a class of 23 pupils at least one pair of children will have identical birthdays is

$$1 - \frac{364}{365} \times \frac{363}{365} \times \ldots \times \frac{343}{365} = .507 \text{ (approx.)}$$

49
The Man, the Boys and the Groceries

THE MAN rows across with the groceries, leaves them on the far side. He then rows back, picks up one boy and takes him across, returning with the groceries. He leaves these on the near side, takes the second boy across and returns for the groceries.

50
Sharing the Wine

THE STEPS required to divide the wine are best understood if they are set out in tabular form:

	8-Quart Container		5-Quart Jar		3-Quart Jar
Start	8		0		0
Step 1	3	→	5		0
" 2	3		2	→	3
" 3	→ 6		2		0
" 4	6		0	→	2
" 5	1	→	5		2
" 6	1		4	→	3
" 7	→ 4		4		0

51
Living to Seventy

IF THE ages of the sons will be a, b and c, then
$$a + b + c = 140 + 3$$
$$\text{and } a + b = 2c + 2$$
$$\text{hence } 3c + 2 = 140 + 3$$
$$\text{and } c = 47$$

If a is one year older or younger than b, a + b must be odd, which is impossible.

If a is one year older than c, the ages will be 47, 48 and 48, which implies that two sons are twins.

Hence a must be one year younger than c and the ages will be 46, 47 and 50.

52
The Barber's Shop

SINCE light has to travel from my back to the mirror behind me, then across the room to the mirror in front of me, and then to my eye, it travels 24 feet, less the thickness of my head, in all.

53
A "Prime" Formula

FOR x = 43 the formula is clearly composite, since 43 will be a factor. Actually the formula gives primes from all values of x from 0 to 41, inclusive.

54
Mix and Match

IF EVERY garment matched, she could make $3 \times 4 \times 3 = 36$ combinations. The exclusion of the jade green blouse with the olive green skirt invalidates 3 of these (one with each sweater). Joan can make 33 different combinations of the three garments.

55
Old Prime's Gourmet Club

BOB MUST be the host since he planned the meal. Louise must be next to Marty since she has met the other husbands at previous dinners. Old Prime can only be on his hostess's left since he would otherwise be next to Louise or June. For Frank to be next to Nancy, Nancy must be on Old Prime's left and Ibby must be the hostess. The seating must be:

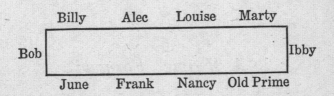

Bob is married to Ibby, Frank to Louise, Alec to Nancy, Marty to June and Old Prime to Billy.

56

The Dispatch Rider

THE CONVOY travels 5 miles in 15 minutes and hence is traveling at 20 miles per hour. If the speed of the rider is x miles per hour, the rider overtakes the convoy at $(x - 20)$ miles per hour and passes it on the return at $(x + 20)$ miles per hour. Hence time to head of convoy and back is

$$\frac{5}{x - 20} + \frac{5}{x + 20} = \frac{1}{3}$$

and the speed of the rider is 40 miles per hour.

A Multiplication Sum

		Line
A B C D		(1)
E F G H I		(2)

	Line
x x x x x	(3)
x x x 2	(4)
x x x 8	(5)
x x x 0 x	(6)
x x x x 0	(7)

---

x x x x x x x x x   (8)

Because of the 0 at the end of line 7 and the 2 at the end of line 4, E must be a 5 and D an even number. Since there are five digits in line 7 and only four digits in lines 4 and 5, G and H must be less than 5. A must be 2, 3 or 4.

We have these possibilities:

A	G & H	D
2	1, 3	4, 6 or 8
2	1, 4	6 or 8
2	3, 4	6 or 8
3	1, 2	4, 6 or 8
4	1, 2	6 or 8

For the 4th or 5th lines to end in 2 and 8 only the second combination listed above is possible and

A = 2   B = 3   G = 1   H = 4   D = 8

The 0 in line 6 then establishes that C = 7 and F = 9.

The solution is 2378 × 59146.

58
A Prime Number Problem

FOR THREE integers to add to 100, one or three of them must be even. 2 is the only even prime.
Losses 67 per cent. Expenses 31 per cent. Profit 2 per cent.

59
Insurance Officers

A puzzle of this type can best be solved by setting out a table of all possibilities and, step by step, indicating the information given. The first sentence tells us Mr. Sprague cannot be the President and the second that Mr. Watson cannot be the President. The next sentence shows that Mr. Lidstone is not the Secretary. We can set out this information thus:

	President	Actuary	Agency	V.P.	Secretary
Mr. Lidstone					X
Mr. King					
Mr. Sprague	X				
Mr. Watson	X				

From the next pieces of information Mr. Sprague cannot be the Actuary and Mr. Lidstone, since he is young, cannot be the President who served in the First World War.

	President	Actuary	Agency V.P.	Secretary
Mr. Lidstone	X			X
Mr. King				
Mr. Sprague	X	X		
Mr. Watson	X			

We now see that Mr. King must be the President since all other possibilities have been excluded, giving:

	President	Actuary	Agency V.P.	Secretary
Mr. Lidstone	X			X
Mr. King	√	X	X	X
Mr. Sprague	X	X		
Mr. Watson	X			

Mr. Watson, since he does not go to the theater or play games, cannot be the Secretary or the Actuary and hence must be the Agency V.P. Mr. Sprague must be the Secretary and Mr. Lidstone the Actuary.

President	Mr. King
Actuary	Mr. Lidstone
Agency V.P.	Mr. Watson
Secretary	Mr. Sprague

60
Cake Eating

CHRISTOPHER should cut a one-inch piece. His second piece should be cut so that his two pieces and John's piece add up to 4 inches. His subsequent cuts should bring the total taken to 7 inches, 10 inches, 13 inches, 16 inches, 19 inches. John then has to take the last one-inch piece. John always took a two-inch piece except for the last and had 13 inches of cake in all so that he felt he had the best of the deal despite the dish washing.

61
Aptitude Tests

	Rule	Answer
(i)	$+1, -1, +1, -1, \ldots$	1 (b)
(ii)	$+0, +0, -3, +0, +0, -3, \ldots$	1 (b)
(iii)	$+2, \times 2, +2, \times 2, \ldots$	60 (c)
(iv)	$\times 2, \div 3, \times 2, \div 3, \ldots$	16 (d)
(v)	$\div 6, \div 5, \times 4, \times 3, \div 2, \div 1, \ldots$	6 (c)

62
The Golden Ratio

IF x is the golden ratio, $x = 1 + \dfrac{1}{x}$

As a decimal $x = 1.618 \ldots$

A Network Problem

CONSIDER the addition of a new line to the network as indicated by the dotted line in I and II. A, P and L will be used to indicate the total number of areas, points and lines.

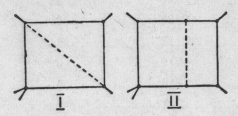

In I, 1 is added to A, P is unchanged and 1 is added to L.

In II, 1 is added to A, 2 is added to P and 3 is added to L. It is stated that there is a simple rule connecting A, P and L. The simplest rule which fits the above analysis is

$$A + P = L$$

However, testing this against the example in the question, we find that $A + P = 13$, while L is only 12. Hence the rule is:

$$A + P = L + 1$$

which equally fits the analysis.

The formula can be proved rigorously by induction.

64
The Binary Scale

SINCE a 1 in the nth position equals 2^{n-1} we need only divide successively by 2 to obtain the answer

	Remainder
2)101	
2)50	1
2)25	0
2)12	1
2)6	0
2)3	0
2)1	1
0	1

Writing the remainders down from the bottom up we get 1100101, which is the expression in the binary scale for 101 in the decimal scale.

The Two Ladders

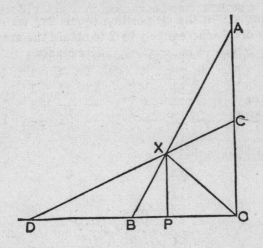

Since $20^2 = 12^2 + 16^2$, $AO = DO$ and $BO = CO$.

∴ $XP = OP$.

Now $\dfrac{XP}{BP} = \dfrac{AO}{BO}$ ∴ $XP = (12 - XP)\dfrac{16}{12}$ and

$7XP = 48$.

The ladders touch at $6\frac{6}{7}$ feet above the ground.

66
Choosing the Weights

THE WEIGHTS can be chosen in eight different ways:

Weights	Possible Choices of Weights							
1 lb.	40	13	4	4	1	1	1	1
3 lb.	—	—	—	—	13	4	1	1
9 lb.	—	—	4	1	—	—	4	1
27 lb.	—	1	—	1	—	1	—	1

67
The Blue Egg

THE FACT that only three different four-digit numbers could be developed from the total score determines this as 17 with the three arrangements 2·5·5·5; 3·4·5·5; 4·4·4·5. The additional information establishes the results as follows:

	Life Ins.	Fire Ins.	Casualty Ins.	Office Efficiency
Philadelphia	5	5	2	5
Boston	3	5	5	4
New Orleans	4	4	4	5

68
The Cigarette Box

EIGHT layers of 16 cigarettes each can be placed in the box, making 128 cigarettes. However, if 16 cigarettes are placed in the bottom layer, 15 in the second layer, 16 in the third layer, and so on, the cigarettes in any particular layer will lie in the dip between the cigarettes in the next lower layer.

The height of the bottom layer will be ⅜ inch but the height of the two bottom layers will be less than ¾ inch. The actual height of these two layers can be calculated by reference to the diagram:

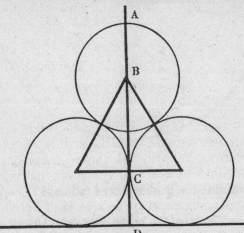

$$AB = \tfrac{1}{2} \times \tfrac{3}{8} \text{ inch}$$
$$BC = \tfrac{3}{8} \times \sqrt{3/2} \text{ inch}$$
$$CD = \tfrac{1}{2} \times \tfrac{3}{8} \text{ inch}$$
$$\therefore AD = \tfrac{3}{8} + \tfrac{3}{8} \times \sqrt{3/2}$$

Similarly the height of nine layers will be:

$$\tfrac{3}{8} + 8 \times \tfrac{3}{8} \times \sqrt{3/2} = 2.98 \text{ inches.}$$

Hence 5 layers of 16 cigarettes and 4 layers of 15, making 140 cigarettes, will fit in the box.

The Goat in the Field

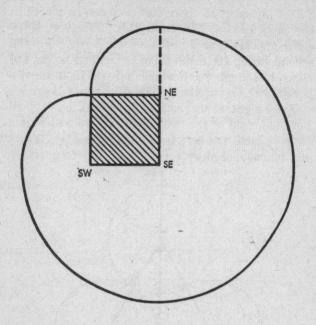

IF WE assume the goat tethered to the S.E. corner of the shack, she can graze an area ¾ of a circle 60 feet in radius from the north, through the east and the south to the west. The area of this is ¾ π 60² sq. feet. When the goat tries to graze on the other side of the shack, her chain will have to go around the N.E. or S.W. corner of the shack. She can only graze two quarters of a circle, each 30 feet in radius with centers at the N.E. and S.W. corners. The area of these two combined is ½ π 30² sq. feet.

Total area grazed is 2,700 π + 450 π sq. feet = 9,900 sq. feet (approx.).

70
School Reports

SINCE the boy received an even number of dimes for the year, he must have received an even number of dimes for each report. Therefore he must have had 1 or 3 A's in each report. Trial soon shows the only possible solution is A, B, C, C, C; A, B, B, B, D; A, A, A, D, D, with a payment of $4.80 for each report or $14.40 for the year.

Old Prime on Bridge

THERE are $2 \times 2 \times 2 \times 2 = 16$ ways in which the four cards may be distributed between the two opponents' hands. Representing the cards by the letters A, B, C and D, the possible distributions may be set out in tabular form as follows:

First Hand	Second Hand	No. of Ways	Number of Rounds Required to Clear
	A B C D	1	4
A	B C D		
B	A C D		
C	A B D	4	3
D	A B C		
A B	C D		
A C	B D		
A D	B C		
B C	A D	6	2
B D	A C		
C D	A B		
A B C	D		
A B D	C		
A C D	B	4	3
B C D	A		
A B C D		1	4

$$\overline{16}$$

The chance that the cards will fall in two rounds is therefore: $\dfrac{6}{16} = \dfrac{3}{8}.$

72
Jigsaw Squares

ADDING together the squares of the numbers immediately establishes that one side must be a multiple of 11, and we soon see that 33 is the only possibility and the solution is then easy.

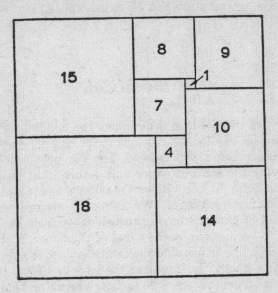

73
The Christmas Gifts

IF x is the number of grandsons and y the number of granddaughters,

$$x^2 = 841 - y^2$$
$$= (29 + y)(29 - y)$$

The two factors must be square numbers or else they must be square numbers multiplied by a common factor. Hence $y = 20$ or 21.

The grandfather had 41 grandchildren.

74
In the Middle

IF THE twisted loop is cut down the middle, a single loop results. The loop is twice as long as the original loop and is twisted. The loop produced by giving the strip of paper half a turn, that is the loop before it is cut down the middle, has most interesting properties. We think of an ordinary sheet of paper as having two sides—a front and a back—separated by the edges of the paper. If you draw a line on one side you cannot pass to the other side without crossing over the edge or lifting the pencil from the paper. Now, take a pencil and start drawing from any point on the uncut loop. Working round the loop, you will find you have arrived at the "other side" of the paper without crossing the edge at any place. Mathematicians say that this loop of paper has only one side. Also the loop, which is known as a Möbius band, has only one edge.

75
Curves of Equal Breadth

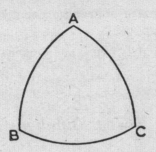

STARTING from an equilateral triangle, ABC, draw the arc of a circle with center A joining B and C. Draw similar arcs with centers B and C. The three arcs will combine to make a curve of equal breadth.

76
The Woltons

FROM the information about bicycle times and speeds we establish that the ratio of the distance to Monk's Wolton and Bishop's Wolton is 4 to 3. Since the three towns are at the corners of a right-angled triangle whose hypotenuse is 5 miles, the actual distances must be 4 and 3 miles, respectively; therefore, the distance to Monk's Wolton is 4 miles.

77
Old Prime's Marbles

82 MARBLES.
>   The boys won 1, 2 and 6 games.
>   The girls won 4 and 5 games.

78
Three Families

THE FAMILIES are:
>   Alex, Effie and Horace
>   Bert, Doris and Iris
>   Joe, Frances and Jeffrey.

79
The Measurement of Time

TAKING age 20 as the base, 1 hour at age 20 plus 1 hour at age 60 seems like $1\frac{1}{3}$ hours at age 20. 2 hours at age x seems like $2\,\frac{20}{x}$ hours at age 20. Hence $2 \times \frac{20}{x} = \frac{4}{3}$ and x equals age 30.

80
The Chain of Weights

ONLY two links need be cut, the 4th and the 11th.

81
Honeycomb Tiling

THE DISTANCE from the center of a tile to the center of any edge is 1 inch. If the tiles were enlarged so that this distance became $1\frac{1}{10}$ inches, no cement would be visible. The areas of the original tile and the enlarged tile are in the ratio 1^2 to $(1\frac{1}{10})^2$ or $1:1 \times 21$. Hence $\frac{21}{121}$ or 17 per cent of the floor covering is cement.

82
Eulerian Square

♥ Q	♠ J	♦ A	♣ K
♦ K	♣ A	♥ J	♠ Q
♣ J	♦ Q	♠ K	♥ A
♠ A	♥ K	♣ Q	♦ J

83
Angles on a Cube

THE LINES BD, DG and BG form the sides of an equilateral triangle so that BD and DG meet at 60°.

84
The Hymn Board

(1) SEVEN each of cards showing 1, 2, 3, 4, 5, 6 and six each of cards showing 0, 7, 8, 9 will be needed, making 66 cards.

(2) If cards showing 6 and 9 are interchangeable, eight of these dual-purpose cards will be needed instead of seven cards showing 6 and six of the cards showing 9. Five fewer cards will be needed.

85
A Party Game

ONE PLAYER should make a small loop in his string. He should thread this loop under the string encircling one of the wrists of the second player, threading it from the second player's arm side towards her hand side. The hand of the second player should then be put through this small loop and then the small loop should be drawn back under the loop of string knotted around the second player's wrist. The two loops will now be separated.

86
Turnpike Driving

THE ANSWERS to the two short puzzles are (1) lower the pressure in the tires and (2) use one nut from each of the other three wheels until he reaches a garage.

Let A travel at x miles per hour and B at y miles per hour.

A overtakes the painter $25/x$ hours before 12:20 p.m.

B meets the painter $21/y$ hours after 12:20 p.m.

The painter takes $4/5$ hours to travel between the two meetings.

$$\therefore 4/5 = 25/x + 21/y$$

Similar calculations in respect of the grass cutter gives

$$4/10 = 10/x + 14/y$$

Solving for $1/x$ and $1/y$ we have $1/x = 1/50$ or $x = 50$ miles per hour. A entered the turnpike at $30/50$ hours or 36 minutes before 12:20 p.m. = 11:44 a.m.

87
Population Growth

AT A rate of growth of 1 per cent a week, 100 becomes 101 after 1 week, $101 \times 1.01 = 102.01$ after two weeks, etc. After 52 weeks we have 168, approximately. Since this is greater than 160, a rate of growth of 1 per cent a week is greater than 60 per cent a year.

A Dice Game

WE MUST first determine the average score which will arise from throwing 1 die. Since 1, 2, 3, 4, 5 or 6 is equally likely to turn up, the average or expected score will be $\frac{1}{6}$ $(1 + 2 + 3 + 4 + 5 + 6)$ $= 3\frac{1}{2}$. Hence with the option of re-throwing one die or declaring it dead, the die should be re-thrown if it is a 1, 2 or 3.

Next, with two dice to throw, the expectation must take account of the fact that if one of the dice falls as a 1, 2 or 3 it will be re-thrown. We must add up all the possible scores and multiply each by the probability of it occurring. Thus $6 + 6$ scores 12 and has a probability of $\frac{1}{36}$, giving an expectation of $12 \times \frac{1}{36}$; $6 + 5$ scores 11 and has a probability of $\frac{2}{36}$, giving an expectation of $11 \times \frac{2}{36}$, and so on. When we get to $6 + 3$ we will assume that the 3 is re-thrown and the expectation is $9\frac{1}{2} \times \frac{2}{36}$.

Working out all these expectations we end up with $\frac{296.5}{36}$ or 8.236.

In the examples given, the 6 must be declared dead in each case. In the first example, since 5 and 4 add up to 9 which is greater than the expectation from throwing the two dice again, both the 5 and 4 will be declared dead. In the second example, 5 and 3 add up to 8. If both are re-thrown, the expectation is 8.236, but if the 5 is declared dead and the 3 re-thrown, the expectation becomes $5 + 3\frac{1}{2} =$ 8.5, so only the 3 should be re-thrown. In the third example both the 4's should be re-thrown.

Of Pigs and Dogs

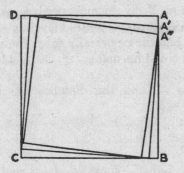

IN THE first very short interval of time, dog A will run due South, dog B due West, Dog C due North, dog D due East. They will be now at the corners of a square, slightly smaller than the original field. The sides of the new square are 200 yards minus the distance traveled by a dog in the short interval of time. Similarly after the next short interval of time the dogs will be at the corners of a square with sides 200 yards minus the distance a dog has traveled since the start of the chase. Finally when they meet, the sides of the square will be zero and each dog will have traveled 200 yards.

Over the Hill

IF I travel at $\frac{5}{6}$ my normal speed, I take $\frac{1}{4}$ hour longer. So it takes $1\frac{1}{2}$ hours bicycling slowly and $1\frac{1}{4}$ hours bicycling normally to go round the hill. If v m.p.h. is the normal speed, the distance round the hill is $\dfrac{5v}{4}$ and the distance to the top is

$$d = \frac{1}{2} \left\{ \frac{5v}{4} - 7 \right\}.$$

Time to the top is $\dfrac{d}{3}$ and time down the other side $\dfrac{d}{2v}$. Equating the sum of these two terms to $1\frac{1}{2}$ hours, we find $v = 12$ miles per hour and $d = 4$ miles. It takes 1 hour 20 minutes to walk to the top of the hill.

91
Drawing an Ellipse

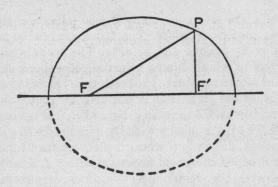

STICK two pins in the paper at points F and F¹, known as the foci of the ellipse. Make a loop of thread equal to FF¹ + FP + F¹P, where P is a point on the ellipse. Place the loop round the pins and round the tip of the pencil. Now it is advisable to get a helper to hold the pins so that they do not pull over. Keeping the loop tight, move the pencil (which should be held vertical) round the ellipse. You will find the pencil will trace out one half of the ellipse exactly. The loop must be shifted to the other side of the pins to trace the second half. If the pins are near together, the ellipse will be close to a circle. If they are apart, the ellipse will be more elongated.

92
Crossing the Desert

DUMPS are set up at A and B, 150 miles and 400 miles along the route. The truck travels to A, dumps 45 gallons and returns. The truck again travels to A and dumps a further 45 gallons and again returns to start. The truck then travels to A, picks up the 15 gallons it has used on route, and travels on to B, dumps 25 gallons at B, and returns to A. The truck fills up with the remaining 75 gallons at A, drives to B where it picks up the 25 gallons dumped there and proceeds, with a full tank, to travel the remaining 750 miles across the desert. It uses 3 loads or 225 gallons in all.

93
Three Sevens

$$\frac{\sqrt{7} + \sqrt{.\dot{7}}}{\sqrt{.\dot{7}}} = 4$$

94
The Missing Dollar

IN THE example Old Prime gave he showed what happened in the case of one win and one loss. Actually there are four possible results, each of which are equally likely, as set out below.

1st Game	2nd Game	Prob-ability	Gain (+) or Loss (—)	Expectation
Win	Win	¼	+ $21	+ $5.25
Win	Loss	¼	— 1	— .25
Loss	Win	¼	— 1	— .25
Loss	Loss	¼	— 19	— 4.75
	Total....	1		ZERO

The greater profit from 2 wins exactly offsets the loss in the three other cases.

95
A Mistake in Surveying

THE SIDES of the triangle formed by the tree (T), House (H) and Barn (B) are in proportion: 5, 4 and 3. Now $5^2 = 4^2 + 3^2$; therefore the angle BTH is a right angle, and the distance from B to the foot of the perpendicular from T to the line BH is
$$150 \times \tfrac{3}{5} = 90 \text{ yds.}$$

See diagram overleaf.

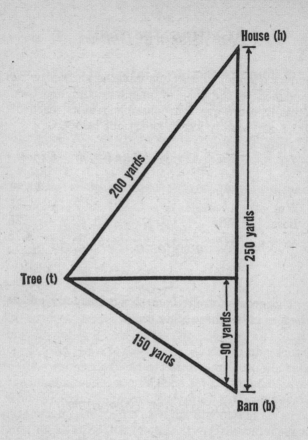

By interchanging the two distances the surveyor will make the foot of the perpendicular from T to the line BH a distance of 90 yards from H instead of from B.

His error will not affect the distance of the tree from the line BH and hence the error in the position of the tree will be

$$250 - 90 - 90 = 70 \text{ yds.}$$

96
Getting the Goat

THE MONEY received from the sale of the cows was a number of dollars which was a square number. All squares which have an odd digit in the tens place have 6 as the final digit. Hence the goat cost $6 and the brother who got the goat should receive ½ ($10 − $6) = $2.

97
The Rhombicosidodecahedron

WE CAN project the vertices, edges and faces of the Rhombicosidodecahedron onto a circumscribed spherical surface so that the edges (E) become lines of a network, the vertices (V) points of a network and the faces (F) areas of a network. In an earlier problem (A Network Problem, No. 63) it was shown that for such a network on a plain surface there was a simple rule connecting E, V and F. The same rule will apply to a network on a spherical surface, except that there will be one additional area (face). We can easily see this by considering the map of an island as being on a plain surface, while the inclusion of the sea as an additional area makes it a map on a globe or sphere. Hence we have V + F = E + 2.

Now in Rhombicosidodecahedron each vertex is the meeting of the ends of four edges and each edge has two ends. Hence E = 2V. Further, since each pentagon has 5 corners, there must be 5 ver-

tices for each pentagon face. Similarly there are 4
vertices for each pair of square faces and 3 vertices for each triangular face. Hence

$$F = \tfrac{1}{5}V + \tfrac{2}{4}V + \tfrac{1}{3}V = \tfrac{31}{30}V$$
$$V - 2V + \tfrac{31}{30}V = 2$$
$$V = 60.$$

There are 60 vertices and 62 faces.

98
The Canal Boat

LET O be John's starting point. Let C be the position of the boat when John starts. Let CA = x
miles, AB = y miles. Then, if John just catches the
boat, CB is twice OB, or

$$2\sqrt{1 + y^2} = x + y$$
$$4 + 4y^2 = x^2 + 2xy + y^2$$
$$3y^2 - 2xy + (4 - x^2) = 0$$

giving $y = \tfrac{1}{3} [x \pm \sqrt{x^2 - 3(4 - x^2)}]$
$$= \tfrac{1}{3}(x \pm \sqrt{4x^2 - 12})$$

If x is less than $\sqrt{3}$, the factor $4x^2 - 12$ will be
negative and y will have no real values. Therefore
the nearest the boat (C) can be to A when John
starts is $\sqrt{3}$ miles. This gives AB = $y = \tfrac{1}{3}\sqrt{3}$
miles = 1016 yards or about $\tfrac{6}{10}$ths of a mile.

99
Old Prime's Boxes

LET THE boxes have sides a, b, (c − 1) and d.
Then $a^3 + b^3 + (c - 1)^3 = d^3$ and $a^3 + 8b^3 - (c + 1)^3 = d^3$

$$\therefore 7b^3 = 2c^3 + 6c.$$

b must be a multiple of 2, and by 'casting out the nines' we can show b is a multiple of 6 (= 6n), c is a multiple of 9 (= 9m) and $28n^3 = 27m^3 + m$. If n does not equal m any solution, if one exists, will make the sizes of the boxes impossibly large and hence n = m = 1. The sides of the boxes are

$$A = 1'' \quad B = 6'' \quad C = 8'' \quad D = 9''$$

100
The Church Tower

IF THE points are indicated by A, B and C and the church by O, AB = 1½ miles, BC = 2 miles and angles AOB and BOC are equal. Therefore AO and CO are in the ratios of 1½ miles to 2 miles, and hence, since AOC is a right-angle triangle, its sides

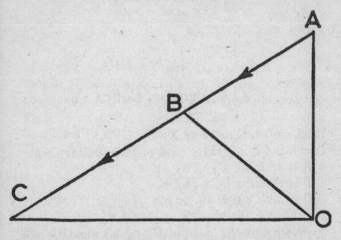

must be in the ratio 3 : 4 : 5. Now AC is 3½ (= 5 × .7) miles therefore OC, the distance from the church, is 4 × .7 = 2⁸⁄₁₀ miles.

101
What, No Digits?

THE KEY to reconstructing the long division is the 8-figure recurring decimal. The value of such a decimal is

$$x \left\{ 1 + \frac{1}{10^8} + \frac{1}{10^{16}} + \frac{1}{10^{24}} + \dots \right\}$$
$$= x \frac{100,000,000}{99,999,999}$$

and the divisor must be a factor of 99,999,999 or a multiple of such a factor. These factors are 3^2, 11, 73, 101 and 137. 3, 11 and 101 produce decimals with shorter recurring periods and hence the divisor must be 73. The full solution is

$$1.\dot{1}5068493\dot{3}$$
$$73\overline{)84}$$

102
The Twelve Coins

CALL non-standard coin X.

Divide coins into three piles of four, calling them:

A containing a_1, a_2, a_3, a_4.

B containing b_1, b_2, b_3, b_4.

C containing c_1, c_2, c_3, c_4.

Operation I. Weigh A/B

Balance means X is in C and all a and b are standard.

Operation II_1. Weigh $c_1 c_2 c_3 / 3$ standard coins.

Balance means X is c_4 and

Operation III_1. Weight c_4/standard solving.

Unbalance gives c_1 c_2 c_3 > standard or < standard. In either case—

Operation III_2. Weigh c_1/c_2 solving.

Unbalance in Op. I gives, say A > B.

Operation II_2. Weigh $a_1 b_1$ + one standard/$a_2 a_3 b_2$ (discarding $a_4 b_3 b_4$)

Balance means X is a_4 heavy, b_3 light or b_4 light, and

Operation III_3. Weigh b_3/b_4 solving.

Unbalance:—if a_1 b_1 s > a_2 a_3 b_2

either a_1 is heavy or b_2 light and

Operation III_4. Weigh a_1/standard solving.

if a_1 b_1 s < a_2 a_3 b_2 then

X is a_2 or a_3 heavy

or b_1 light, and

Operation III_5. Weigh a_2/a_3 solving.

103
The Round Hole

THE MAXIMUM-sized round cylindrical hole will have as its axis a line joining two diagonally opposite corners (e.g., the top left corner of the front of the cube and the bottom right corner of the back of the cube). Looked at along this axis the cube will appear as in the illustration overleaf.

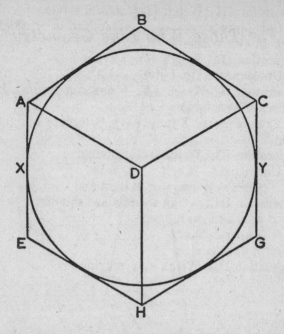

The evaluation of the diameter of the hole is not quite as simple as it looks, because the above figure is in three dimensions. We can calculate that XD = $\sqrt{5}$ inches, but XD is not perpendicular to the axis of the cylindrical hole. However AC is at right angles to the axis, the line of sight, and is equal to XY. The theoretical maximum diameter of the hole is therefore

$$2\sqrt{2} = 2.828 \ldots \text{inches.}$$

If the theoretical maximum-sized hole is drilled, the remaining portion of the cube will fall into six parts.

For Those Who Like Geometry

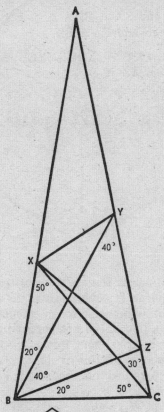

DRAW BZ so that $\widehat{ZBC} = 20°$

Join XZ.

Now $\widehat{BZC} = 180° - \widehat{BCZ} - \widehat{ZBC}$

$\qquad = 180° - 80° - 20° = 80°$

$\therefore \widehat{BZC} = \widehat{BCZ}$

and $BZ = BC.$

Similarly $\widehat{BXC} = 50° = \widehat{BCX}$

$\therefore BX = BC = BZ$

$\widehat{XBZ} = 60°$ and $BX = BZ$ $\therefore \triangle \widehat{BXZ}$ is an equilateral triangle and $XZ = BZ$.

Again $\widehat{BYZ} = 180° - \widehat{YBC} - \widehat{YCB} = 40° = \widehat{YBZ}$

$\therefore YZ = BZ = XZ$

$\therefore \widehat{ZXY} = \widehat{ZYX}$

Now $\widehat{YZX} = 40°$ $\therefore \widehat{XYZ} = 70°$ and $\widehat{XYB} = 30°$.

Old Prime's Crossnumber Puzzle

¹2	²8	³5	⁴7	⁵1	⁶4	⁷1	⁸9	⁹1	¹⁰3
¹¹5	0	0	5	¹²3	0	8	¹³8	0	9
¹⁴7	8	6	¹⁵8	3	7	¹⁶3	4	1	9
¹⁷1	0	1	¹⁸8	1	¹⁹4	9	²⁰1	5	5
²¹3	²²6	²³2	8	8	0	²⁴9	0	²⁵1	4
²⁶5	8	4	7	²⁷1	4	7	²⁸1	8	5
²⁹3	3	1	³⁰2	7	0	³¹4	5	1	1
³²6	8	3	8	³³3	1	4	1	5	9

NOTES

7, 21 *and* 33 *Across* can be completed immediately.

1 *Across*   Let Z be the number, n the multiplier and a the first digit.

$$Z \times n = 10Z - a(10^6 - 1)$$

$$\therefore (10 - n)Z = a(10^6 - 1) \text{ whence}$$

n = 3 and Z = 142857 or 285714.

6 *Down*   The first digit must be 4 or 7. $5^3 + 6^3 + 7^3$ is less than 700 and $0^3 + 7^3 + 8^3$ is

greater than 800 so 7 is impossible. 407 is the only solution and 1 *Across* is 285714.

11 *Across* is multiple of 1001, hence 2 *Down* is 808 and 17 *Across*, 101.

1 *Down* The cube root must be 127, 131, 137 or 139. Only 137 fits, giving 2571353.

The remainder of the solution is reasonably straightforward, but will take time.